IMAGINE THAT™

Licensed exclusively to Imagine That Publishing Ltd
Tide Mill Way, Woodbridge, Suffolk, IP12 1AP, UK
www.imaginethat.com
Copyright © 2021 Imagine That Group Ltd
All rights reserved
0 2 4 6 8 9 7 5 3 1
Manufactured in China

Written by Georgina Wren
Illustrated by Gabi Murphy

ISBN 978-1-80105-000-5

A catalogue record for this book is available from the British Library

Daddy Loves Me

Written by
Georgina Wren

Illustrated by
Gabi Murphy

My daddy says he loves me,
he says it every day,

But he doesn't have to say it,
I know it anyway.

When we go into town,
he holds my hand in his.

That's so he knows where I am,
and I know where he is!

If I'm very hungry, and I can't wait till we get back,

I never need to worry,
Daddy always brings a snack.

When I go to nursery,
I'm not sad – I just have fun!

Daddy will come back for me, when the day is done.

If I'm playing in the sandpit, Daddy likes to join in too.

We put flags on our sandcastles –
I like red, Daddy likes blue.

When I'm going to a party, Daddy helps me brush my hair.

I want to look
so smart, when all
my friends are there.

When we are at the playground,
we do all my favourite things!

I zoom down the slide, and Daddy pushes me on the swings.

We love baking cupcakes,
and Daddy says I'm a good cook.

I do all the hard bits,
Daddy reads the recipe book.

I sit on Daddy's shoulders
when we go out
to explore.

Daddy holds me tight,
and I can see much more!

When I wake up at night,
and it's as quiet as can be,

I shout to wake up Daddy,
and he comes to comfort me.

I know my daddy loves me,
I told you I can tell.
He really, really loves me ...

... and I love him so much as well.